Musical Reflections of Ireland

25 of the very best Irish Songs & Dance Tunes, arranged for Guitar, Easy Piano, Keyboards, Harp, Accordion and Melody Instruments

Musical Reflections of Ireland

25 of the very best Irish Songs & Dance Tunes, arranged for Guitar, Easy Piano, Keyboards, Harp, Accordion and Melody Instruments

selected and arranged by John Loesberg

harmonizations by Sarah Greenham

OSSIAN

part of The Music Sales Group

London / New York / Paris / Sydney / Copenhagen / Berlin / Madrid / Tokyo

Báidín Fheilimí 20

The Banks Of The Suir 18

The Cliffs Of Dooneen 7

Danny Boy 34

Drowsy Maggie 26

An Fhaillingín Mhuimhnach 37

Give Me Your Hand 14

The Green Bushes 24

If I Were A Blackbird 38

Love Is Pleasing 22

The Maids Of Ardagh 9

Miss Murphy 40

A Munster Jig 36

My Lagan Love 32

Oft In The Stilly Night 10

The Poor Irish Boy 25

The Rose Of Tralee 46

The Sally Gardens 8

Sheebeg And Sheemore 12

Sir Charles Coote 30

Slievenamon 42

The Sligo Fancy 48

The Spanish Lady 28

The Star Of The County Down 16

The White Cockade 44

Published by
Ossian Publications
8/9 Frith Street, London, W1D 3JB, UK.

Exclusive Distributors:
Music Sales Limited
Distribution Centre, Newmarket Road,
Bury St Edmunds, Suffolk, IP33 3YB, UK.

Music Sales Corporation
257 Park Avenue South, New York, NY10010
United States Of America.

Music Sales Pty Limited
120 Rothschild Avenue,
Rosebery, NSW 2018, Australia.

Order No. OMB42
ISBN 0-946005-36-2

Originally published in 1998.
This edition © Copyright 2005
Novello & Company Limited,
part of The Music Sales Group.

Special thanks to Sarah Greenham for her excellent
harmonies and Andrew Shiels for his typesetting.

Design & cover photograph by John Loesberg.

The words of some of the songs have been included
in this album. For complete versions of hundreds of
Irish songs, together with background notes see:

Folksongs and Ballads popular in Ireland Vols 1, 2, 3, 4
edited by John Loesberg (Ossian).

www.musicsales.com

The Cliffs Of Dooneen

Song

It's a nice place to be on a fine summer's day,
Watching all the wild flowers that ne'er do decay,
Oh, the hare and the pheasant are plain to be seen
Making homes for their young round the Cliffs of Dooneen

Take a view o'er the mountains, fine sights you'll see there;
You'll see the high rocky mountains on the west coast of Clare,
Oh, the towns of Kilkee and Kilrush can be seen,
From the high rocky slopes round the Cliffs of Dooneen.

So fare thee well to Dooneen, fare thee well for a while,
And although we are parted by the raging sea wild,
Once again I will wander with my Irish Colleen,
Round the high rocky slopes of the Cliffs of Dooneen

The Sally Gardens

In a field down by the river, my love and I did stand
And on my leaning shoulder, she laid her snow-white hand.
She bid me take life easy, as the grass grows on the weirs;
But I was young and foolish and now am full of tears

Down by the Sally Gardens, my love and I did meet,
She passed the Sally Gardens, with little snow-white feet.
She bid me take love easy, as the leaves grow on the tree;
But I, being young and foolish, with her did not agree.

The Maids Of Ardagh

Polka

Oft In The Stilly Night

Air

10

'The Devil's Punchbowl', Killarney

Sheebeg And Sheemore

O'Carolan (1670-1738)

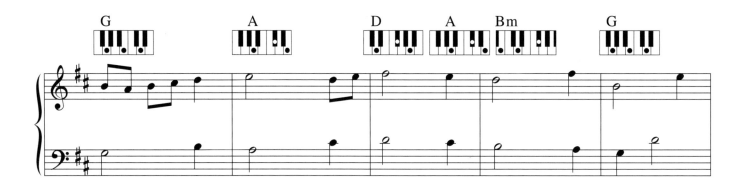

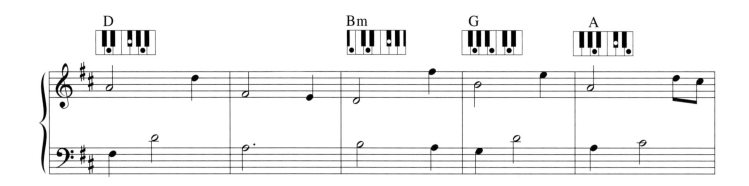

Give Me Your hand

Ruari Dall O'Cathan (17th Cent)

The Star Of The County Down

Song

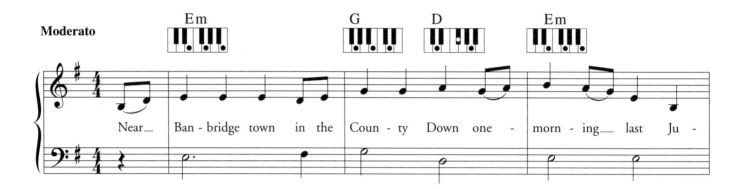

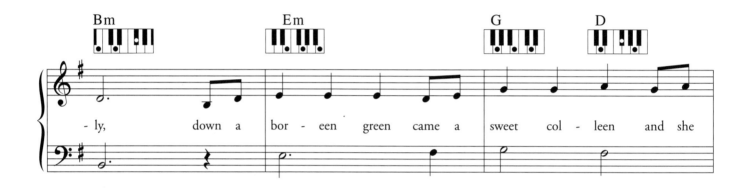

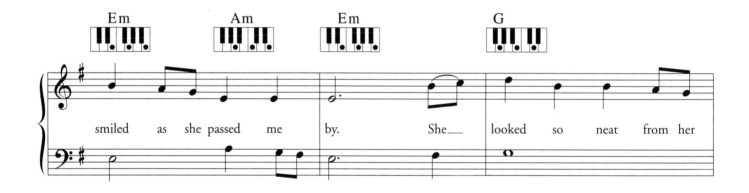

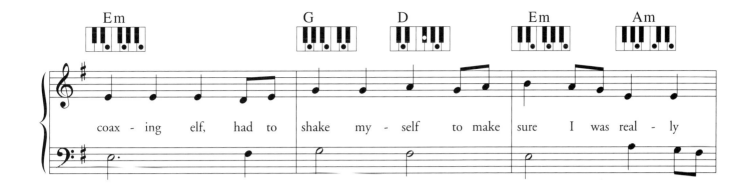

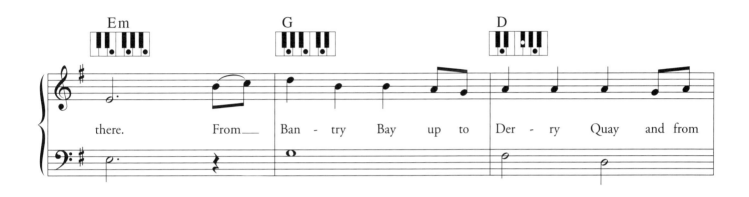

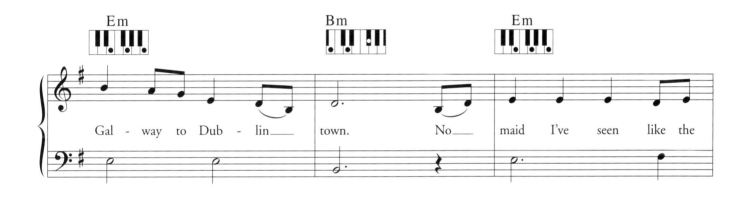

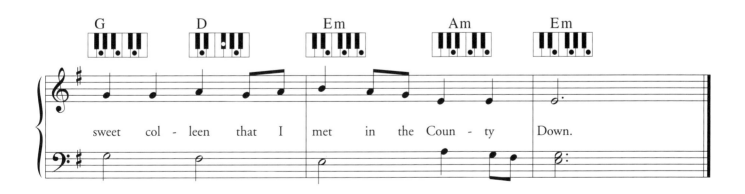

The Banks Of The Suir

Báidín Fheilimí

Song

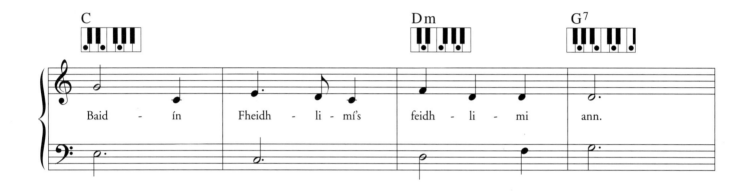

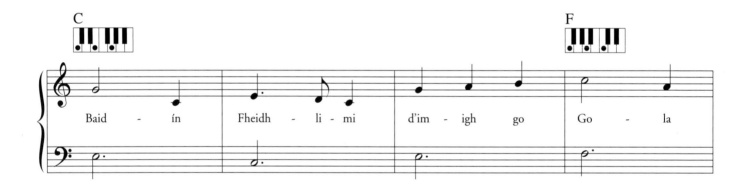

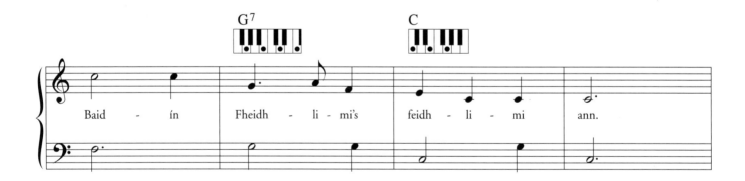

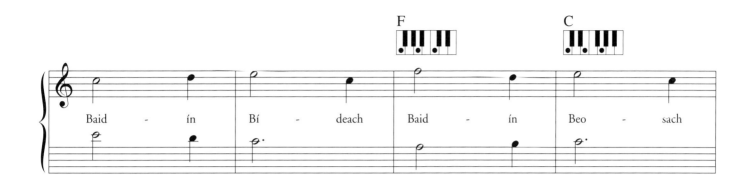

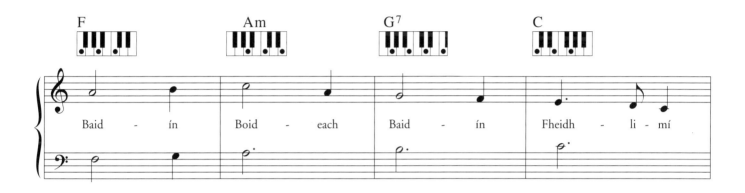

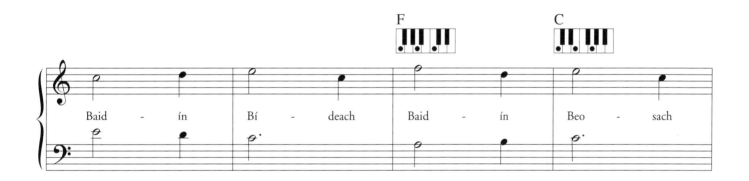

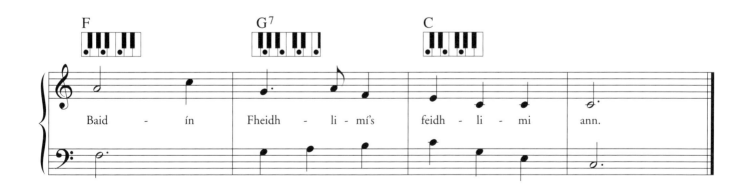

Love Is Pleasing

Song

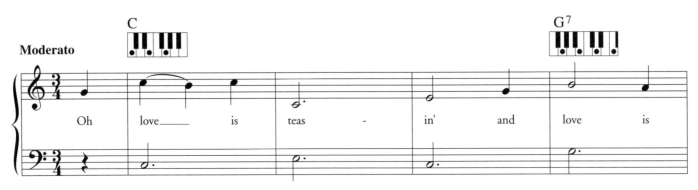

Oh love____ is teas - in' and love is

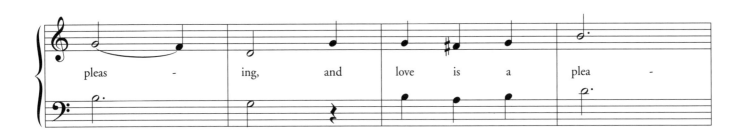

pleas - ing, and love is a plea -

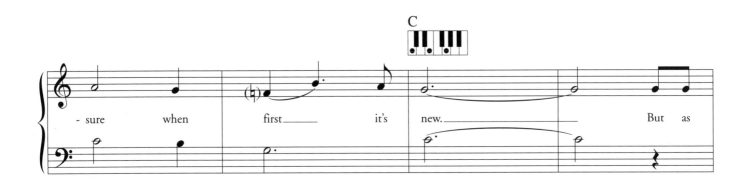

- sure when first____ it's new.____ But as

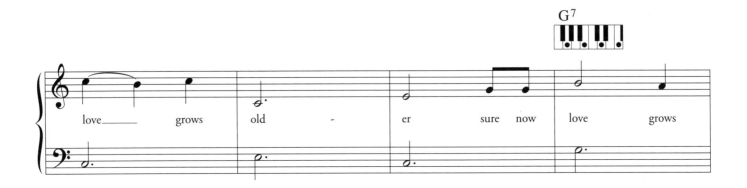

love____ grows old - er sure now love grows

cold - er, 'til it fades a - way

C

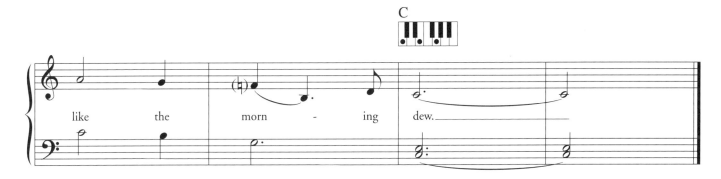

like the morn - ing dew._____

I wish, I wish, I wish in vain
I wish, I wish I was a maid again.
But a maid again I never can be
'Til apples grow on an ivy tree.

But the sweetest apple is soonest rotten
And the hottest love is the soonest cold
But what can't be cured, love, must be endured, love,
So now I am bound for Amerikay

St. Kevin's Church, Glendalough

The Green Bushes

Air

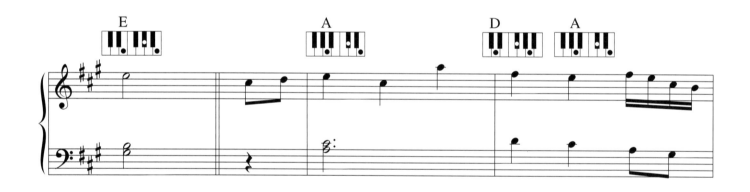

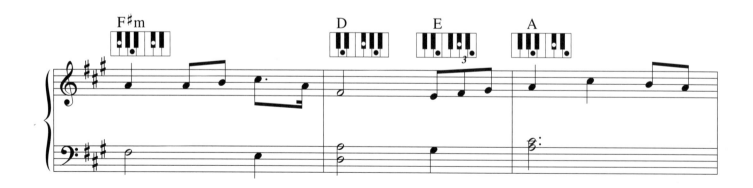

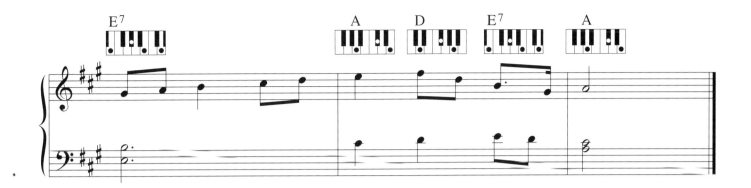

The Poor Irish Boy

Air

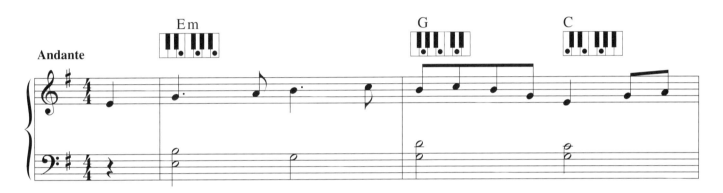

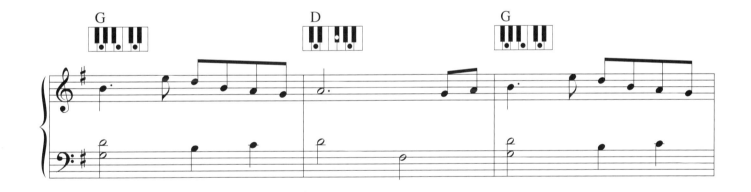

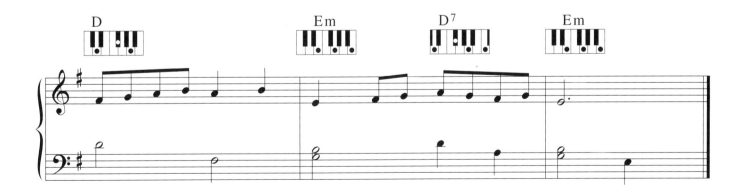

Drowsy Maggie

Reel

Carrickfergus

The Spanish Lady

Song

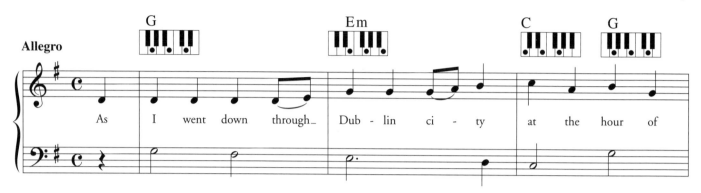

Allegro

As I went down through_ Dub - lin ci - ty at the hour of

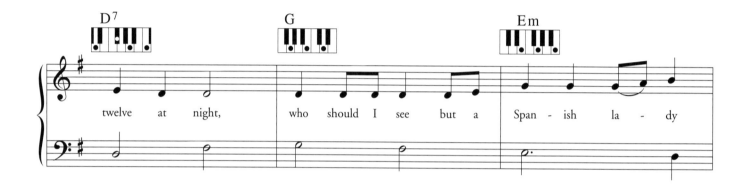

twelve at night, who should I see but a Span - ish la - dy

wash - ing her feet by can - dle light. First she washed them,

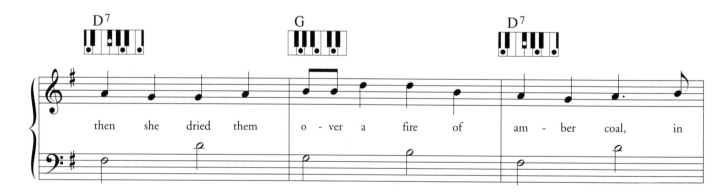

then she dried them o - ver a fire of am - ber coal, in

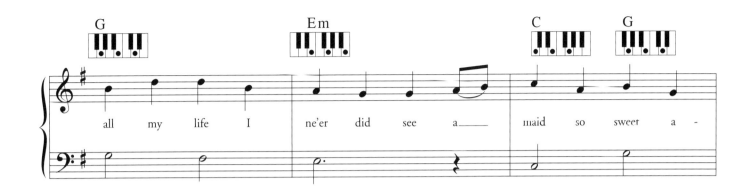

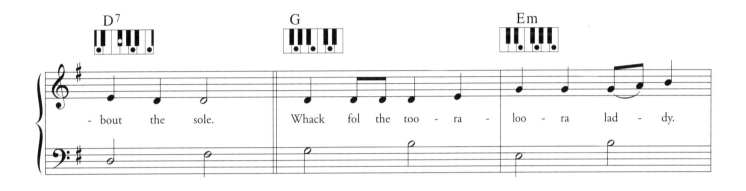

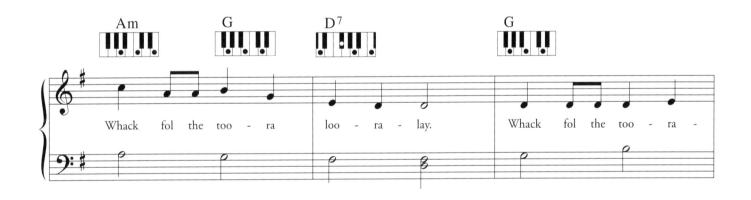

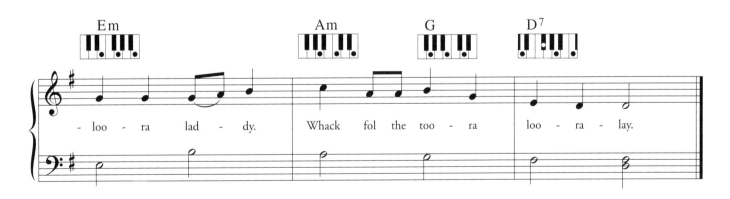

Sir Charles Coote

O'Carolan (1670-1738)

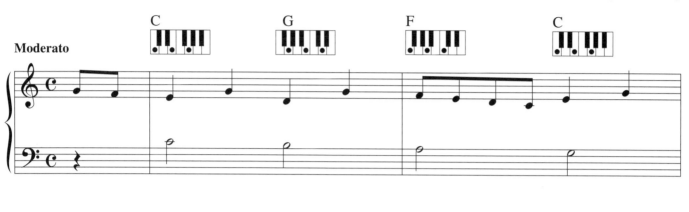

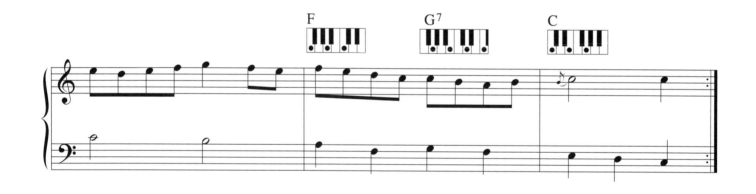

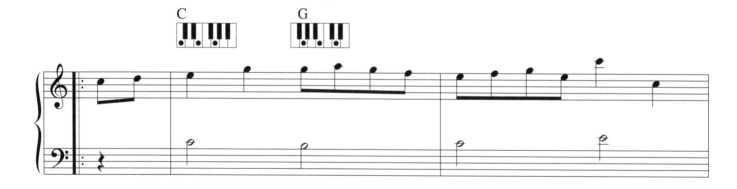

Galway

31

My Lagan Love

Song

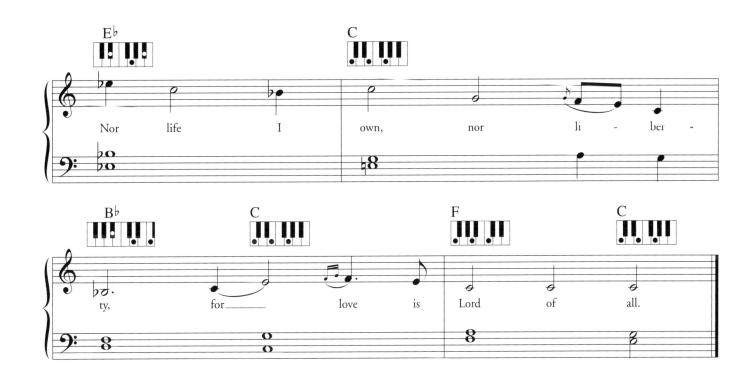

And often when the beetle's horn, hath lulled the eye to sleep
I steal unto her shieling lorn and through the dooring peep;
There on the cricket's singing stone, she stirs the bogwood fire,
And hums in sweet, sad undertone, the song of heart's desire.

Her welcome, like her love for me, is from the heart within
Her warm kiss is felicity that knows no taint or sin;
When she was only fairy small her gentle mother died.,
But true love keeps her memory warm, by Lagan's silver side.

Danny Boy

Song

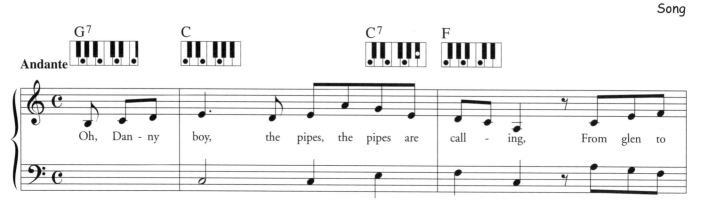

Oh, Dan - ny boy, the pipes, the pipes are call - ing, From glen to

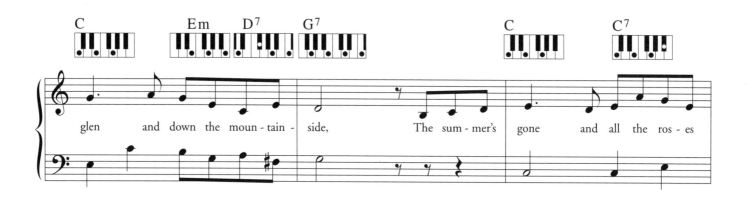

glen and down the moun - tain - side, The sum - mer's gone and all the ros - es

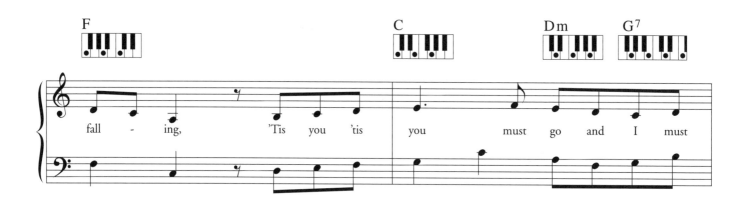

fall - ing, 'Tis you 'tis you must go and I must

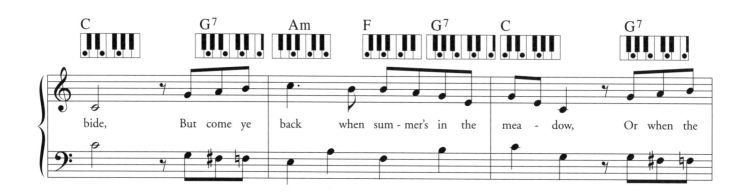

bide, But come ye back when sum - mer's in the mea - dow, Or when the

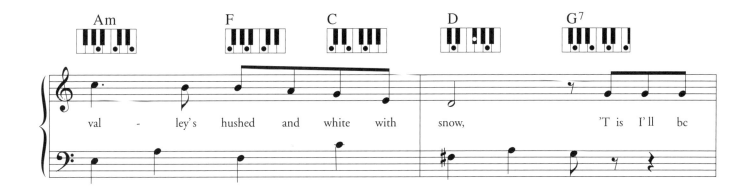

val - ley's hushed and white with snow, 'T is I'll be

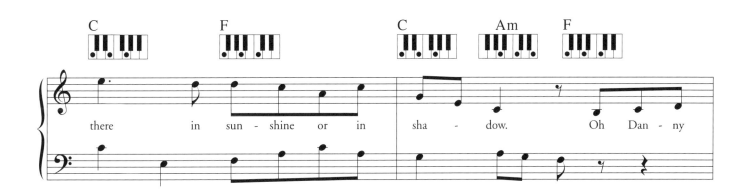

there in sun - shine or in sha - dow. Oh Dan - ny

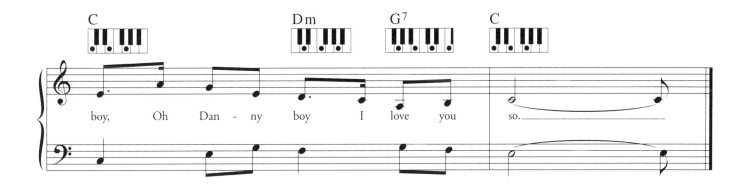

boy, Oh Dan - ny boy I love you so.

A Munster Jig

An Fhaillingín Mhuimhneach

Air

If I Were A Blackbird

Song

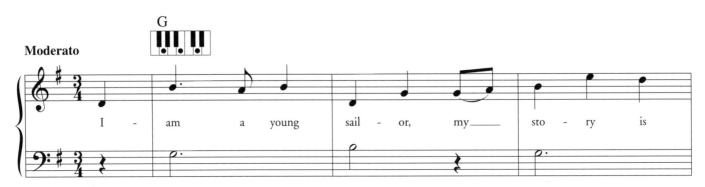

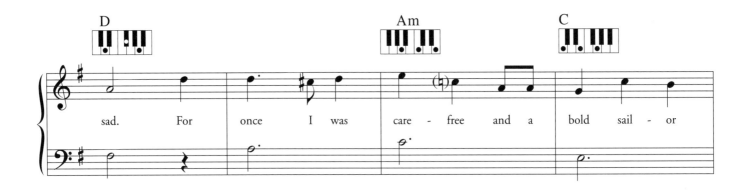

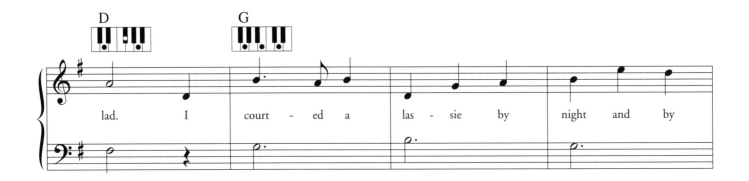

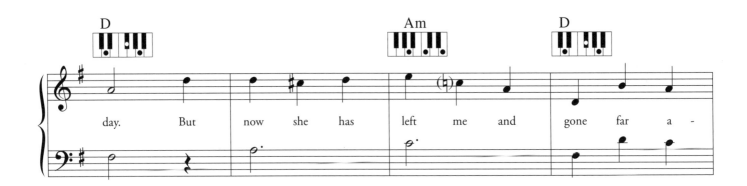

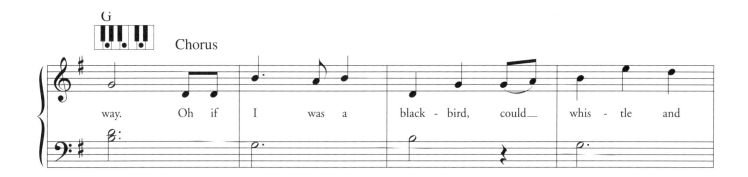

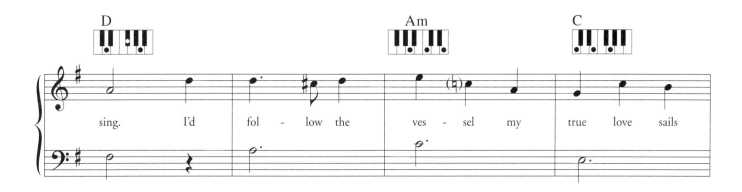

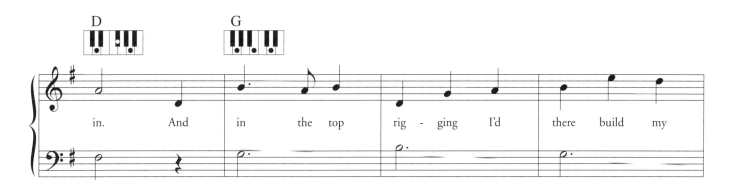

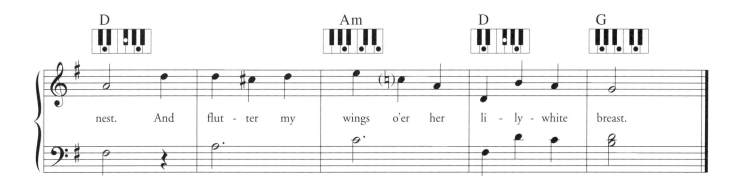

He promised to take me to Donnybrook Fair
To buy me red ribbon to bind up my hair.
And when he'd return from the ocean so wide,
He'd take me and make me his own loving bride

His parents they slight me and will not agree
That I and my sailor married should be.
But when he comes home I will greet him with joy
And I'll take to my bosom my dear sailor boy.

Miss Murphy

O'Carolan (1670-1738)

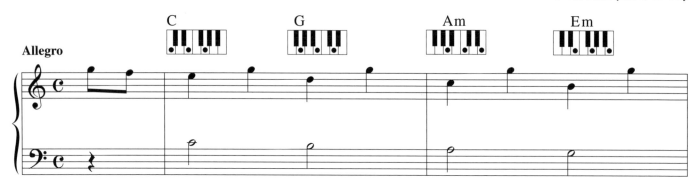

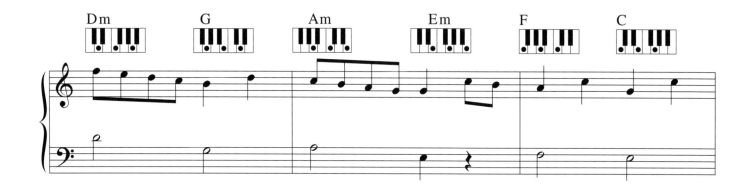

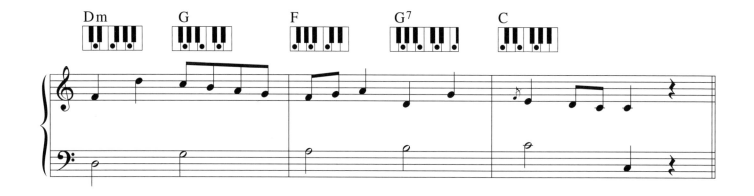

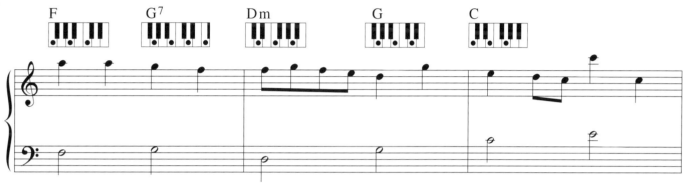

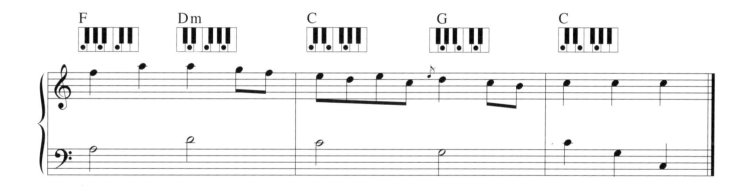

Slievenamon

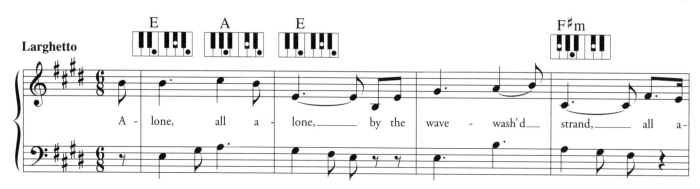

A - lone, all a - lone,___ by the wave - wash'd___ strand,___ all a-

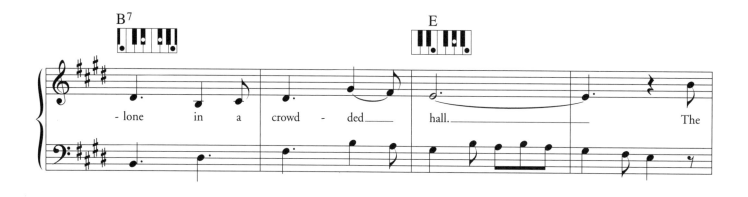

- lone in a crowd - ed___ hall.___ The

hall it is gay___ and the waves they are grand___ but my

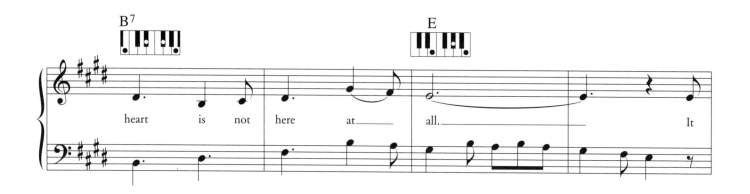

heart is not here at___ all.___ It

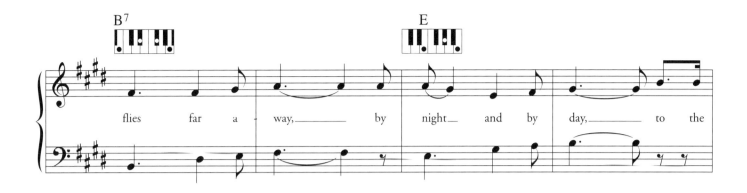

flies far a - way,_____ by night___ and by day,_____ to the

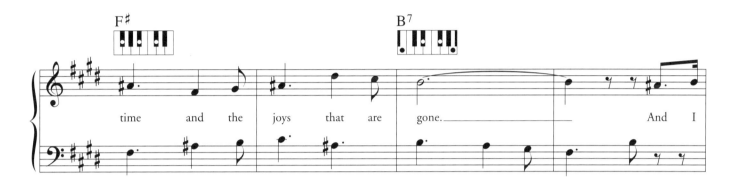

time and the joys that are gone._____ And I

nev - er can for - get____ the sweet maid - en I met,_____ In the

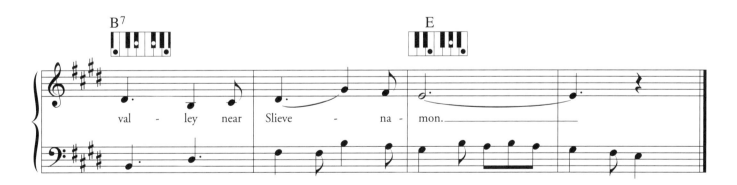

val - ley near Slieve - na - mon.____

It was not the grace of her queenly air
Nor the cheek of the rose's glow.
Nor her soft black eyes, not her flowing hair
Nor was it her lily-white brow.
'Twas the soul of truth and of melting ruth,
And the smile of summer's dawn
That stole my heart away, one mild summer day,
In the valley near Slievenamon.

In the festive hall, by the star-watched shore
My restless spirit cries:
'My love, oh, my love, shall I ne'er see you more,
And my land, will you ever uprise.
By night and by day, I ever, ever pray.
While lonely my life flows on
To our flag unrolled and my true love to enfold,
In the valley near Slievenamon'.

The White Cockade

March

Trim Castle

The Rose Of Tralee

Song

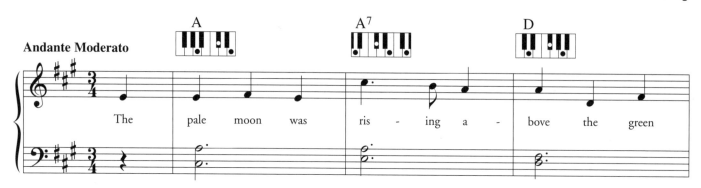

The pale moon was ris - ing a - bove the green

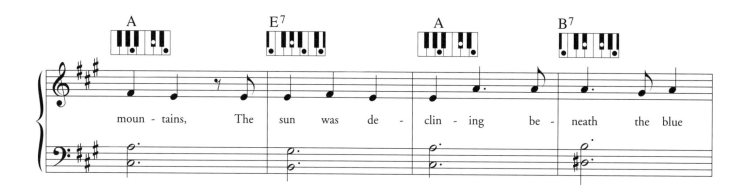

moun - tains, The sun was de - clin - ing be - neath the blue

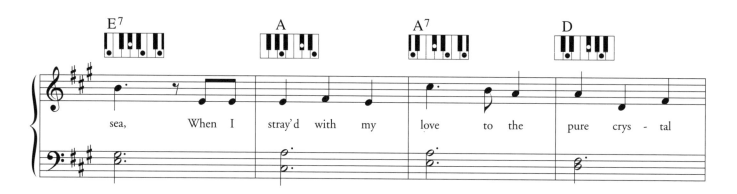

sea, When I stray'd with my love to the pure crys - tal

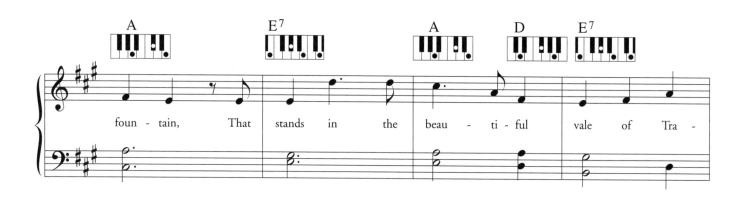

foun - tain, That stands in the beau - ti - ful vale of Tra -

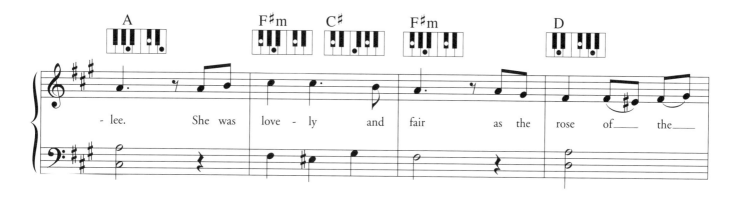

- lee.   She was   love - ly   and   fair   as the   rose   of___ the___

sum - mer,   Yet   'twas   not   her   beau - ty   a - lone   that won

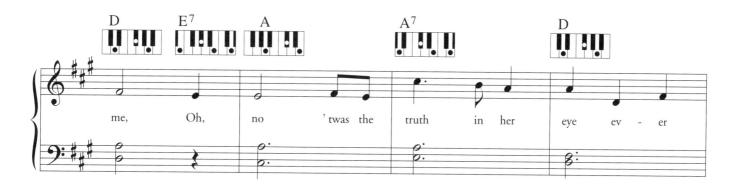

me,   Oh,   no   'twas the   truth   in   her   eye   ev - er

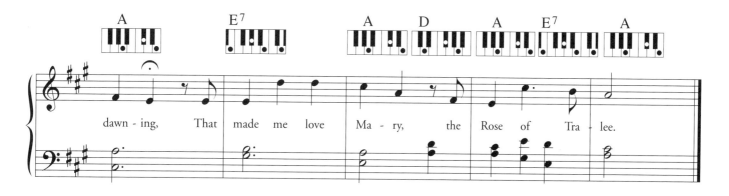

dawn - ing,   That   made   me   love   Ma - ry,   the   Rose   of   Tra - lee.

The cool shades of evening their mantles were spreading.
And Mary, all smiles, sat list'ning to me,
The moon thro' the valley, her pale rays were shedding
When I won the heart of the Rose of Tralee.
Tho' lovely and fair as the rose of the summer,
Yet 'twas not her beauty alone that won me,
O, no, 'twas the truth in her eye ever dawning,
That made me love Mary, The Rose of Tralee.

The Sligo Fancy

Hornpipe